S0-BFC-222

THE BREMEN TOWN-MUSICIANS

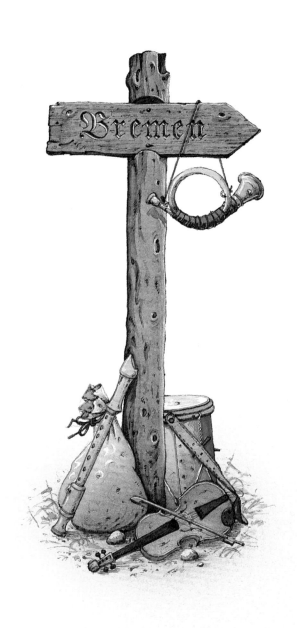

The Bremen Town-Musicians

Illustrated by Kestutis Kasparavičius
Put into verse by James Krüss
English adaptation by Pauline Hejl

ess!inger

6. edition 2003

© 1994 Esslinger Verlag J.F.Schreiber, Esslingen
Anschrift: Postfach 10 03 25, 73703 Esslingen
Alle Rechte vorbehalten (14339)
ISBN 3-480-20076-1

A donkey, old and tired out,
Is of no use, there is no doubt.

If he cannot carry his heavy load
His master gives him no abode.

The donkey thinks: "Oh woe is me!
He'll have me killed, that I can see!"

His mind made up, and off he goes
To Bremen, for that town he knows.

"I'll play the drum in the Town Hall
And there'll be food enough for all."

And just as he is passing by,
A poor old dog gives such a sigh.

"You are too old", his master said,
"And good for nothing, except dead."

The donkey says, "Well come with me!
Play the horn and then we'll see.

Away we go to the Town Hall
And there'll be food enough for all."

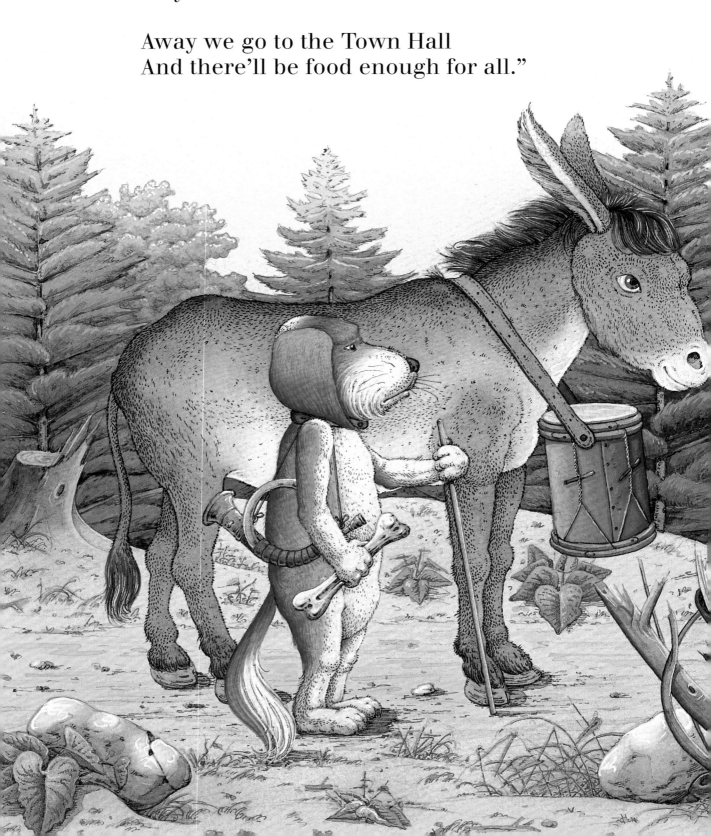

The two of them walk on and on,
And then a cat they come upon.

"To catch the mice I'm now too old,
I'll soon be drowned, so I've been told."

The donkey says, "Well come with me,
And sing and play, for now we're three.

Away we go to the Town Hall
And there'll be food enough for all."

So off they go across the land,
Then see a woman, knife in hand.

A poor old cock she wants to kill,
A tasty soup would be a thrill.

The donkey says, "Well come with me,
If you can sing, then we shall see.

Away we go to the Town Hall
And there'll be food enough for all."

Cock and donkey, cat and dog
Set off for Bremen in a jog.

But Bremen is a long, long way,
So overnight 'tis here they stay.

They make a fire and all lie down
And start to dream of Bremen town.

"Good night, sleep tight", the cock cries out,
"Tomorrow we must be about."

The cock however sees a light
Shining through the dark dark night.

"I wonder what that light could be?
Let's walk across then we shall see."

So up they get and stretch and groan,
"We're still so tired", they all moan.

Whoever's there is not alone
And dog thinks: "Have they got a bone?"

Oh yes, there's sausage, bones and wine
And fruit and pudding tasting fine.

"I'm not so sure", the donkey says.
"These people have such funny ways."

The cat is wary too and cries:
"Look all around you, use your eyes!

All these jewels are of the best,
I think we've found a robbers' nest!"

Upon each other's backs they climb,
Ready, steady, now's the time.

Together they are such a sight,
And give the robbers a great fright.

The donkey goes hee-haw, hee-haw,
The old dog growls and shakes a paw.

Miaow, miaow, the old cat cries,
The cock crows loud and up he flies.

At the window they now stand
And terrify the robber band.

The robbers all get up and flee,
The four friends jump and laugh with glee.

The table's full of things to eat:
Chicken, sausage, wine and meat.

The house is nice, not at all creepy,
The four friends find they are now sleepy.

They wish each other a good night,
Then go to bed, switch off the light.

The robbers stand beneath the trees,
Annoyed and angry, not at ease.

Then one says, "I know what to do,
The window's open, push me through.

Whoever gave us such a fright
Now will have to face a fight."

When indoors he sees a light.
That's what he thinks, but he's not right.

For what he sees are the cat's eyes,
The robber's in for a surprise!

The cock and cat, they scratch and bite,
The donkey kicks, puts up a fight.

The dog bites hard, the robber flees
And runs away beyond the trees.

The four now have, with food and goods,
A life of pleasure in the woods.

And every day they sing a song,
For here they feel they now belong.

"Here in the woods we'll sing and play,
And not to Bremen go,
For Bremen is so far away,
As we four friends well know."